Contents

1.1 What's the book about?

1 Look at the picture on the front cover of this book.

    a Where does this story take place?

    b What is happening?

2 Make sentences that are true for you. Then explain your answers to another student.

    a I *believe / don't believe* in ghosts.

    b I *have / have never* seen a ghost.

    c I *have / have never* heard a ghost.

    d I *know someone / don't know anyone* who has seen a ghost.

    e If I ever see a ghost, I will *laugh / scream*.

3 Look at these pictures of ghosts. Which is most like your idea of a ghost? Tick (✓) one.

1.2 What happens first?

1 The first story is called 'Room 7'. Read the words in *italics* and look at the picture on page 1. Tick (✓) the best answers.

    a Where is Room 7, do you think?

      ☐ In a hotel.   ☐ In a school.   ☐ In a hospital.

    b Is the man in the car

      ☐ going to have an accident? ☐ going to see a ghost? ☐ a ghost?

2 What will be in Room 7, do you think? Write your ideas.

....

Room 7

*I closed my eyes tightly. I didn't feel afraid. Not then. Fear came later.
No, I wasn't afraid; but I wanted to think ...*

Perhaps you don't believe in **ghost**s. I'm not sure that I believe in them. I'm not sure that I saw a ghost that night. But if I didn't see a ghost, what did I see?

I was returning from a business trip to the north. I lived near London then. It was winter. The roads were covered with ice, and I had to drive slowly and carefully. I was still a long way from home when it got dark. Then my car lights began to fail. It was too dangerous to stay on the main road. I turned off into a quiet country road.

After a few kilometres I saw a road sign – *Millham*. Five minutes later I was driving along a narrow street. There were a few shops with bright lights, and I could see a garage at the end of the street. I stopped there and explained my problem. The man looked at my car lights.

ghost /gəʊst/ (n) a dead person who has returned to Earth. Some people believe that you can see *ghosts*.

'I'll repair them in the morning,' he said.

'Is there a hotel in Millham?' I asked.

'There's The Goat at the top of the street,' he said. 'We don't have many visitors in Millham in the winter. Tell Mr Richards I sent you. He'll look after you.'

I thanked him and took my suitcase out of the car. Then I walked back up the street to The Goat. It was an old building. The hotel office was just inside the front door. A big man came through another door at the back of the office and smiled at me in a friendly way.

'Mr Richards?' I asked.

'Yes,' he answered. 'Can I help you?'

I explained that my car was at the garage. 'I need a meal and a room for the night,' I said.

'The meal isn't a problem,' he said. 'Dinner will be ready in an hour. But this is a small hotel. We've only got six bedrooms, and they're all full.'

The door opened again, and a little woman walked quickly into the room.

'This is my wife,' Richards explained. He turned to her and said, 'I was telling our visitor that we're full tonight, Liz. His car's at the garage, and he wants dinner and a bed for the night.'

'There's Room 7, Tom,' she said.

'But we don't ... ' he began.

'We can't send him away on a night like this,' his wife said. 'I'll make the bed in Room 7.'

'I'm giving you trouble, I'm afraid,' I said.

'It's no trouble, Mr ... ?'

'Saunders,' I said. 'I'm John Saunders.'

'It's no trouble, Mr Saunders. We don't use Room 7 much. There's nothing wrong with it.' She gave her husband a look when she said that. He didn't reply.

Room 7 was on the top floor, above the other bedrooms. It felt quite cold, but there was an electric fire.

'It will soon get warm,' I thought. 'And it's beautifully quiet up here. I'll sleep well tonight.'

It wasn't a big room. There was a bed, a cupboard, and a **washbasin** behind the door. Between the washbasin and the cupboard was a big, straight-backed chair.

I washed, and then went down to dinner. I enjoyed my meal and then I went to the bar. I talked to Richards and some of his friends until I began to feel sleepy.

---

washbasin /ˈwɒʃˌbeɪsən/ (n) a large bowl in a bathroom. You use it for washing your face and hands.

'I think I'll go up to bed now,' I said.

'Goodnight, then, Mr Saunders,' Richards said. 'I hope you'll be comfortable. Sleep well!'

◆

I don't know how long I slept. Something woke me. It wasn't a noise. The bedroom was quiet, but something strange was happening. The light on my bedside table wasn't on, but part of the room was slowly becoming light. My bed was in the dark. I couldn't see the cupboard or the washbasin, but I could see the big chair. I could see its seat, its arms, its legs and its tall, straight back. It was shining at me out of the dark.

I closed my eyes tightly. I didn't feel afraid. Not then. Fear came later. No, I wasn't afraid; but I wanted to think and to shut out that strange light.

'I dreamt it!' I thought. 'Of course! I drank too much in the bar after dinner and I was dreaming.'

I decided to count slowly up to fifty and then to open my eyes again.

'Forty, forty-one ... ' I was counting the numbers very slowly when I heard it. Somebody was **breathing** in the room. This was not a dream. A thief, perhaps?

I opened my eyes. Now a man was sitting in the chair. He was old, and he had white hair, but he was sitting up straight. His bright eyes were looking at me.

I tried to speak, but no words came. I wanted to say, 'Who are you? What are you doing here?' But I couldn't. I told myself not to be afraid. He was too old to hurt me. But his eyes were frightening. They never moved.

He lifted his left hand and pointed his finger at me. Now his eyes were very sad, and suddenly I wasn't afraid of him. When he spoke, his voice was tired.

'I never knew,' he said. 'But you do.'

His hand dropped. Suddenly, I could speak. 'What do I know?' I asked. 'Who are you? What ... ?' Before I could complete the question, he – and the light – disappeared.

A voice woke me. 'Here's a cup of tea, Mr Saunders. Your breakfast will be ready in half an hour.' Richards put the tea on my bedside table and went out quickly.

I thought about my strange visitor. Did I dream it all? I decided not to worry Mr and Mrs Richards with a mystery that they couldn't solve.

I had my breakfast. Then I went into the hotel office to pay my bill. Mrs Richards was sitting at the desk.

She smiled and gave me the bill. 'Did you sleep well?'

I looked up to answer her. I saw a picture on the wall behind her. The white hair, the strong face and the bright eyes were terribly **familiar** to me.

I pointed at the picture. 'Who's that?' I asked.

She looked at the picture and turned back quickly. 'It's Tom's father. He lived with us here at The Goat. He died five years ago in the room that you slept in last night. That's why Tom didn't want you to have Room 7.'

'But you ... ' I stopped. She was speaking again.

'There were some silly stories about Room 7, Mr Saunders,' she said. 'One or two nervous visitors thought that the room was **haunted**. A ghost isn't good for a hotel, so Tom's father decided to sleep there. He didn't believe in ghosts. So he went up to bed at his usual time, but ... '

---

breathe /briːð/ (v) to take air into your body and let it out again
familiar /fəˈmɪljə/ (adj) known to you because you have seen it before
haunt /hɔːnt/ (v) (of ghosts) to appear somewhere often

'Yes?' I said. 'What happened?.'

'I took tea up for him the next morning,' she said. 'And I found him in that big chair – cold and dead. Of course, he was an old man. His heart just failed suddenly.'

I picked up my case. 'Mrs Richards ... ' I said.

She wasn't listening to me. She smiled and said, 'So we never discovered the mystery of Room 7. And I don't believe that anybody will. It's just a silly story.'

I paid the bill, said goodbye and walked quickly down the street towards the garage. The voice of an old man seemed to follow me. 'I never knew,' it said. 'Was Room 7 haunted? I never knew. But you do. You know now, don't you?'

2.1 Were you right?

Look back at Activity 1.2 on page iv. Then put these in order, 1–8.

a ☐ A ghost is sitting in the chair in his room.

b ☐ There is a strange light in the room.

c ☐ His car lights stop working.

d ☐ Mr Saunders doesn't tell Mrs Richards about his ghostly visitor.

e ☐ Mr Saunders goes to the bar for a drink after dinner.

f ☐1 Mr Saunders is travelling on business.

g ☐ Mrs Richards gets Room 7 ready.

h ☐ The Goat has only one empty room.

2.2 What more did you learn?

1 Complete the sentences with these names.

Mr Richards   Mr Saunders   Mrs Richards   Tom's father   an old man

a .... doesn't want to use Room 7.

b .... is happy for Room 7 to be used.

c .... thinks he will sleep well in Room 7.

d .... is sitting in the chair in Room 7.

e .... brings Mr Saunders a cup of tea in the morning.

f .... didn't believe in ghosts, but now he is one.

2 Circle the things that Mr Saunders does *not* say are in Room 7.

2.3 Language in use

1 **Look at the sentence on the right. Then finish the sentences below. There are a number of possible answers.**

> I don't know **how long I slept**.

a Mr Saunders' car lights start failing. He doesn't know how far ....

....

b He arrives at The Goat. He doesn't know how many ....

....

c He is offered a room. He doesn't know how much ....

....

2 **Now complete each of these sentences with a word from the box.**

| what   where   why   who   how |

a Mr Saunders doesn't know .... his lights aren't working.

b He doesn't know .... he can spend the night.

c He doesn't know .... the strange light in his room is.

d He has no idea .... the old man got into his room.

e Later, he realises .... the old man was.

f He understands .... Mr Richards didn't want him to sleep in Room 7.

2.4 What's next?

1 **Read the title of the next story and the words in *italics* below it. Discuss these questions.**

a What does an empty house look like, from outside?

b Is Mrs Wood in the house, do you think?

2 **Look at the pictures on pages 8 and 9. Circle the best answers.**

a What kind of town is this?

- dangerous

- exciting

- quiet

b What is the man doing in the town?

- He is on holiday.

- He is writing a story for a newspaper.

- He lives there.

c How are the two people on the sofa feeling?

- worried

- happy

- bored

Mrs Wood Comes Home

There were curtains at the windows. The house didn't look empty.
'Are you still there, Mrs Wood?' I thought.

I always went to Porchester for my holidays. It's a quiet little town, full of interesting old buildings, and I was studying its history.

I'm not a rich man and I can't stay in hotels, but Jack Thompson invited me to stay in his pretty little house in Fore Street. He and I were at school together. I had some very happy times with him and his wife, Annie, until ... until Mrs Wood came home.

That year, I went to Porchester as usual. It was a fine spring afternoon when I arrived. We went for a walk and I took photographs of the church. That night after supper, we sat talking by the fireside.

'Tell me all the news,' I said.

Jack smiled. 'Life moves very slowly here, Bill,' he said. 'We've got a new doctor – Dr Warren – if that interests you.'

'Everything about Porchester interests me,' I said. 'Tell me more.'

'Mrs Wood has gone away,' Annie said.

'Mrs Wood?' I said. 'Where did she live?'

Annie smiled at me. 'In the house across the street. The one with the big tree in front of the windows. She's very old. She didn't go out very much because she can't walk very well.'

'I often thought that somebody was looking out of an upstairs window,' I said. 'But the tree covers part of it.'

'Mrs Wood spent most of her time looking out of that window.' Jack spoke angrily, and I was surprised.

'She was lonely, Jack,' Annie said. 'She liked to watch people. She wanted to know what was happening outside.'

'She was lonely because she was rude to people,' said Jack. 'She was very rude to you. Remember?'

'We agreed not to talk about that again,' said Annie. 'Just before Christmas, Bill, she went to stay with her son in Australia. I always felt sorry for her.'

'I feel sorry for her son,' Jack said. 'It won't be very nice for him with that old woman in his house. But I hope she stays with him for ever. I don't want her back here.'

I could see that they were both becoming angry. I was surprised. But I asked about the new doctor, and we didn't talk about Mrs Wood again.

I went to bed quite early, but I couldn't sleep. I was thinking about Jack and Annie. Why were they so angry about Mrs Wood? Annie was, I thought, as angry as Jack. But she was trying to hide her feelings.

I got out of bed, went to the window and looked across the street at Mrs Wood's house. The moon was shining brightly and I could see the front of the house clearly. The **leaves** of the big tree moved slowly in the wind.

leaf /liːf/ (n) one of the small, flat, green parts of a plant

There were **curtains** at the windows. The house didn't look empty. 'Are you still there, Mrs Wood?' I thought.

Then I saw the curtain at one of the upstairs windows move. Mrs Wood was watching me!

I turned away from the window and jumped into bed. I lay there in the dark and felt very, very frightened.

Slowly, I grew calmer. 'You were wrong!' I said to myself. 'You only *thought* that curtain moved. The wind pushed the leaves across the window. And if Mrs Wood *is* there, she can't hurt you. She's a lonely old woman. You're a strong, healthy man. What are you afraid of? But she's not in her house. She's in Australia, with her son.'

I felt better then, but I didn't sleep for a long time. And in my dreams I was trying to escape from a strange, dark house. An old woman was watching me.

I felt tired and unhappy when I woke up the next morning. My holiday was starting badly. I washed and dressed. Then I opened my bedroom window. I took a photograph of Mrs Wood's house before I went downstairs.

Jack was alone in the kitchen. 'What's the matter?' he asked. 'You look tired.'

'I didn't sleep very well.'

'Annie had bad dreams too,' he said. 'She's staying in bed. She was dreaming about that old woman who lived across the road.'

We didn't talk much while we ate.

After breakfast, I said, 'Why did you get angry last night when you were talking about Mrs Wood?'

'Annie tried to help her,' he said slowly. 'She went shopping for her, and often cooked for her. She sat and talked to her. Or she sat and *listened* to her. The old woman prefers to talk, not listen.'

'Did you go across there with Annie?' I asked.

'No,' he said. 'I never liked her. One day Annie came back, looking tired and ill. I asked her what was wrong. Mrs Wood was very rude to her, and frightened her ... Annie never went there again. She couldn't forget ...'

Jack's story wasn't very clear, but I understood the general meaning. The old woman knew that Jack didn't like her. Jack is a good, kind man, but she hated him. She didn't listen to Annie. 'You're as bad as your husband,' she shouted at her. 'I'll get you both out of your house.'

I waited until Jack finished speaking. Then I said, 'Mrs Wood is a terrible old woman, but she can't hurt you. Why don't you just forget about her?'

Jack looked at me. 'Why didn't you sleep last night?'

◆

curtain /ˈkɜːtn/ (n) a piece of hanging cloth that is pulled across a window

I didn't enjoy my holiday. Jack and Annie were kind to me, but at night they didn't sit talking by the fireside. They stood and looked through their front window at Mrs Wood's house. And each night, from my bedroom, I thought I saw her face at her window. I was glad when my holiday finished. Now I could escape from Porchester.

A few days after I got home, the postman **deliver**ed my holiday photographs. Usually, I enjoyed looking at them. But this time I was afraid to open the packet.

At last I opened it. Slowly, I searched through the photographs. Then I found the one that I feared to see.

There it was – the photograph of Mrs Wood's house. I felt sick. Everything was clear and bright – the garden, the tree, the front door. And, at an upstairs window, an old woman's face was looking through the glass!

I was holding the photograph when the door of my flat flew open. Jack ran into the room. I tried to hide the photograph, but he pulled it out of my hand.

'There she is,' he said. 'That ... thing ... is Mrs Wood.'

'But, Jack, that's not possible. She's a long way away ...'

He stopped me. I shall never forget his words or the terrible look on his face as he spoke.

deliver /dɪˈlɪvə/ (v) to take something to a place

'Mrs Wood died in Australia on your first day in Porchester,' he said. 'We heard the news after you left.'

'But how do you explain ... ?' I pointed to the photograph.

'I can't,' he said. 'I only know that ... she came home.'

A new fear came over me. 'Annie!' I shouted. 'Jack, how is Annie? Does she know that Mrs Wood came home?'

He looked old and ill. I thought that he was going to fall. I put my hand on his arm and guided him to a chair. At last he spoke, but his voice was weak.

'Last night there was a knock at our door,' he said. 'Annie went to open it. I was in the kitchen, but I could hear her voice. I shall never forget her cry. "Mrs Wood," she said. "You've come home!" I ran to the door. Annie lay there – dead. She died of fear.'

3.1 Were you right?

Look back at your answers to Activity 2.1. Two of these sentences aren't true. Which ones? Put a cross (✗) next to them.

1 ☐ Bill goes to Porchester on holiday.

2 ☒ Annie and Mrs Wood are very good friends.

3 ☐ Annie and Jack are upset when they talk about Mrs Wood.

4 ☒ Bill sleeps very well at his friends' house.

5 ☐ Mrs Wood hated Jack when she lived in the house opposite.

6 ☐ The ghost of Mrs Wood is seen in Bill's photograph.

3.2 What more did you learn?

1 **Who says these words after Annie's death, perhaps? Match the faces to the names.**

Mrs Wood's son

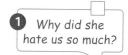
1 Why did she hate us so much?

Bill

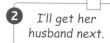
2 I'll get her husband next.

Jack

3 We must bring my mother's body back to Porchester.

Mrs Wood's ghost

4 I will destroy the photograph.

2 **Why was Mrs Wood so rude and unpleasant when she was <u>alive</u>, do you think? Why is her ghost so terrible? Talk to other students.**

3.3 **Language in use**

Look at the sentence on the right. Then choose a word from the box below to complete these sentences.

> I had some very happy times with him and his wife, Annie, **until** Mrs Wood came home.

| after so because before but until when |

1 It was a fine spring afternoon .... I arrived in Porchester.

2 Mrs Wood didn't go out much .... she couldn't walk very well.

3 The moonlight was bright, ... I could see her house clearly.

4 I took a photograph of Mrs Wood's house .... I went downstairs.

5 Jack is a good, kind man, ... she hated him.

6 Anne was kind to Mrs Wood .... the old woman was rude to her.

7 My holiday photographs arrived .... I got home.

3.4 **What's next?**

1 Do you know a place where something frightening happened in the past? Where is it? What happened? Tell the class.

2 Read the title of the next story and the words in *italics* below it. Then look at the picture on pages 16 and 17. Talk to another student. What do you think happens in this story? Make notes.

Notes

A Ghost in the Garden

Knock ... knock ... knock.
There, at the bedroom window. Slow, heavy knocks.

I worked hard in the city all my life. Then, when I was sixty years old, I decided to stop. I wanted to live in the country, with a big garden where I could grow flowers and vegetables. My wife agreed. She was born in the country and wanted a quiet life. So we started to look for a house.

We travelled a long way to look at houses. When we saw a *For Sale* sign, we stopped. But none of the buildings pleased us. We searched for months and became very tired.

At last, we found the house of our dreams. In a small village, about eighty kilometres from the city, we discovered Samways. Nobody was living there,

and it was just right for us. It was built of stone. It was warm, sunny and comfortable. Between the front of the house and the quiet village street was a little garden. At the back there was a bigger garden, full of fruit trees and flowers.

We moved into Samways in the late spring. It was an old house and it needed a lot of work. We bought tables, chairs, cupboards and beds. We had to get curtains too. We were careful that everything looked nice. This was our home now, for the rest of our lives.

The garden was wild when we arrived. But we worked hard, and by the end of August, our garden was almost as beautiful as our house.

One afternoon in September, I was working alone in the garden. My wife was in the house, making some tea. I heard her calling to me through the open window of the living-room. 'Henry,' she called. 'Tea's ready and we've got a visitor. Father Barnes has come to see us.'

Father Barnes was the village **priest**. This was his first visit to our house.

'I'm glad that you've come,' I said.

'It's a beautiful old house,' the priest answered. 'Everybody in the village is pleased that you're living here. You're making a wonderful difference to the house and garden.'

'Thank you,' I said. 'When we've had tea, you must have a look at the big garden at the back.'

'I'd like to do that,' he answered. 'I'm very interested in gardens. But I don't get much time to work in mine.'

'You must be busy,' Joan said. 'Do you visit most people in the village?'

'I think the village priest should know everybody,' he said. 'I knew that you and Mr Chapman were busy. So I haven't come to see you before today. But I've noticed you both in church.'

While we had tea, we talked about the village. Father Barnes told us a lot about its history. Joan and I both liked him. He seemed to be a good, kind man and a good priest.

After we finished our tea, we went into the garden. Father Barnes knew quite a lot about gardens too, and that pleased us. Gardeners enjoy talking about their gardens. Then we walked back towards the house.

'Do you know how your house got its strange name?' he said.

'No,' said Joan. 'Do you know?'

'It was built by a man called Samways,' Father Barnes said. 'In the country a house is often given the name of its builder. Elijah Samways built your house more than 200 years ago. He was a rich man, and he built it for himself.'

'Did he have a family?' I asked.

'No,' Father Barnes said. 'He lived here alone, without wife or children. He had one old **servant** – a man.'

'What happened when he died?' Joan asked.

'His house was sold,' Father Barnes said. 'Nobody with his name has lived here since then. But now you've bought his house and its name is still Samways. That's quite nice, isn't it?'

We agreed that it was. Then I remembered something.

'We've got one other big job in the garden,' I said. 'Look at this tree.'
I pointed at a big tree near the wall of the house. Its **branch**es were nearly touching our bedroom window.

'We'll have to cut it down,' I said. 'It's too near the house. It will be dangerous when the winter winds come.'

priest /priːst/ (n) a religious person who works in a church
servant /ˈsɜːvənt/ (n) someone who works in another person's house
branch /brɑːntʃ/ (n) one of the parts of a tree that grow up and out from it

Before Father Barnes could reply, Joan spoke. 'Oh, no, Henry,' she said. 'We've talked about this before.' She turned to the priest. 'Tell him that he's wrong, Father. It's a beautiful, healthy tree. It's wrong to cut it down.'

The priest looked at the tree for a long time. 'I must say that I agree with Mrs Chapman,' he told me. 'It's a beautiful tree. I don't think it's dangerous. You can cut those top branches if they're too long. But I don't think you should cut the tree down. It was growing here before Elijah Samways built the house.'

'We won't do anything in a hurry,' I said. 'We'll wait until winter comes. Then we'll decide.'

◆

Winter came late that year. The long, hot summer was followed by a warm, dry autumn, and I didn't think about the big tree. Then, in early November, the winds began and the rain came. We sat in our comfortable living-room during the day. We read books and listened to music. At night, we had our evening meal and went to bed early. Sometimes during the day, I put on my raincoat and went into the garden. I couldn't do any work there, but I watched the big tree.

In the strong wind the branches looked like arms moving high above my head. They seemed to send a message to me, but I couldn't read their signs.

One day I stood out there longer than usual, and Joan called to me from the house. 'Henry! What are you doing out there in the rain?'

'I'm coming, dear,' I answered.

But before I returned to the house, I climbed up the tree. I cut the two branches that were near our bedroom window. Father Barnes was right, I thought. The tree was strong and healthy. There was no need to cut it down. But I felt safer when those branches were shorter.

I told Joan and she smiled at me. 'I'm so glad that you agree, Henry,' she said. 'Now, take off your wet coat.'

At the end of November, the winter storms got worse. We lay in bed at night and listened to them. We fell asleep at last with the sound of the wind in our ears. And when we were sleeping, it was in our dreams.

On November 30th – I can't forget that date – I woke up in the middle of the night. Joan was sitting up in bed.

'What's the matter?' I asked. 'Can't you sleep?'

'Ssh! ... Ssh! ... Listen!' she said.

I listened, but I could only hear the sound of the wind.

'What's the matter?' I asked her again. 'What are you afraid of?'

'There's a noise,' she said. 'I can't hear it now, but it woke me up. Somebody was knocking at the window.'

'Joan, dear, don't be silly!' I said. 'You were dreaming. Lie down and go to sleep.'

'I'm not being silly, Henry,' she said. 'Somebody or something is knocking at that window.'

I got out of bed. 'I'll go down to the kitchen and make you a hot drink,' I said. 'You're too nervous to sleep.'

Before I could open the bedroom door, she called to me. 'I'm coming too, Henry. Don't leave me here. Listen!'

And this time I heard it.

Knock ... knock ... knock.

There, at the bedroom window. Slow, heavy knocks. Loud enough to hear above the sound of the wind.

Knock ... knock ... knock.

I moved towards the window. Then I stopped. I was afraid to pull back the curtains. I was afraid to look through the window.

While I stood there, Joan spoke again. 'It's all right, Henry,' she said. 'I know what it is. Those long branches are knocking against the window in the wind.'

But the branches were too short to reach the window now. Before I could say anything, she pulled back the curtains. Then she screamed; and my heart seemed to stop.

The face of an old man was looking through the window. His long, white hair was moving in the wind, and he was holding up his hands. He began to hit them against the window ... knock ... knock ...

'Dear **God**!' I cried. 'Shut him out!'

I pulled the curtains across the window and put my arm round Joan.

God /gɒd/ (n) the one who made Heaven and Earth, in some religions. Other religions have a number of *gods*.

'Come with me,' I said. 'We'll go down to the kitchen.'

She put her hand in mine and I took her to the door.

'His eyes, Henry!' she said. 'Did you notice his eyes? They were sad ... terribly sad eyes, Henry.'

Daylight came at last. The wind was weaker now and the morning was cold and bright. At nine o'clock I telephoned Father Barnes. He came and listened to our story.

'An old man's face, you say?' he asked. 'With long, white hair?'

'Yes,' I said.

'Did he seem angry?' asked Father Barnes. 'Did he want to frighten you?'

'Oh no!' Joan answered the question before I could speak. 'No, Father, he seemed to be asking for help. I'm sorry we didn't help him. We were too frightened.'

The priest spoke gently. 'Of course you were afraid. But I think that perhaps you *can* help him.'

'How?' I asked. 'You seem to know something about the man, so please tell us. If this terrible thing happens again, we won't be able to stay in this house.'

'I think I can solve the mystery,' he said. 'Elijah Samways lived here with one old servant. I told you that, but I didn't tell you the rest of the story. One night, thieves killed Elijah Samways and stole all his money. The thieves were never caught. The old servant, Robert Forester, was **accuse**d of letting them into the house. "I'm **innocent**!" he said. "I was asleep all night." But nobody believed him. He was a poor old man with no family and no friends, and ... and they **hang**ed him in this garden, from a branch of the big tree. They hanged an innocent man.'

'You believe that he was innocent?' I asked.

'I do now. I believe that he was wrongly accused,' said the priest. 'He came to you last night to ask for help.'

'Why did he come last night?' I asked.

'It was November 30th,' said Father Barnes. 'They hanged Robert Forester on that date, 200 years ago.'

'How can we help him?' asked Joan.

'We must show him that we believe in his innocence.'

'But how can we tell him?' asked Joan.

'Follow me,' said Father Barnes. And he took us into the garden, to the big tree. 'They **bury**d Robert Forester here.'

---

accuse /əˈkjuːz/ (v) to say that someone has done something wrong

innocent /ˈɪnəsənt/ (adj) not a criminal

hang /hæŋ/ (v) to kill someone by *hanging* them from something around their neck

bury /ˈberi/ (v) to put something under the ground and cover it

'Here?' I said. 'But this isn't **holy** ground.'

'No,' said the priest. 'But we'll make this holy ground. We'll **pray** for Robert Forester.'

The priest got down on his knees, and Joan and I did the same. He prayed for Robert Forester, and we prayed with him. He prayed for that innocent man. He asked God to forgive Robert Forester's enemies. Then he took off the cross that he wore round his neck. He planted it in the ground. Now the ground was holy.

'He'll rest now,' said the priest.

And we went back into the quiet house.

holy /ˈhəʊli/ (adj) very religious
pray /preɪ/ (v) to speak to your god. You usually want to ask for help or to thank the god.

4.1 Were you right?

Look back at your answers to Activity 3.4. Then draw lines to make sentences.

1 Henry and Joan move to the country

2 Henry wants to cut down the tree

3 Joan can't sleep

4 It isn't the tree branches

5 Joan screams

6 The ghost of Robert Forester is at the window

because something is knocking at the window.

because Henry cut them back.

because it can't rest.

because it is too near the house.

because they want to grow flowers and vegetables.

because there is a face at the window.

4.2 What more did you learn?

1 What is happening in these pictures?

2 You suddenly learn that a man was killed in your house. Another man was hanged in your garden. This happened many years ago. Will you stay in the house? Will you sell the house and move? Ask other students.

Language in use

Look at the sentence on the right. Use the past passive form of the verbs to complete these sentences.

> The old servant, Robert Forester, **was accused** of letting them into the house.

1   Your house .... (build) by a man called Samways.

2   Samways's house .... (sell) after he died.

3   A long, hot summer .... (follow) by a warm, dry autumn.

4   We .... (wake up) by the sound of the wind.

5   Elijah Samways .... (kill) by thieves.

6   An innocent man .... (hang) in the garden.

7   Robert Forester .... (bury) in the garden.

8   Finally, he .... (put) to rest by the priest.

What's next?

1   **Look at the picture of Roger Wingate's new car on pages 28 and 29. He thinks it is a good car at a good price. Why do you think the price is low?**

- ☐ It uses a lot of petrol and is expensive to run.
- ☐ It has been in an accident.
- ☐ There is something wrong with it.

Or write your idea: ....

2   **Are you a nervous person? Talk to other students and discuss these questions.**

a   You are walking along a quiet road at night. A cat suddenly runs in front of you. Do you scream, laugh or not notice?

b   You are listening to your iPod. Someone touches your shoulder. Do you jump or scream? Or do you ask what they want?

c   You are driving alone in your car. Someone suddenly speaks. What do you do?

Roger Wingate's New Car

A voice spoke very quietly. It was – or it seemed to be – a woman's voice. 'Turn right here,' it said.

'How much?' he asked.

The answer surprised and pleased Roger. The car was big, but the price was low.

'And it's only a year old?' he said.

'That's right,' said the man at the garage. 'One year old. We know the man who owned it. We sold it to him. Now we're selling it for him. He's decided to stop driving. We've looked after it since it was new. It's a good car. At this price, it's a *very* good car.'

Roger thought hard. The garage man was right. It was a good car and the price was very, very good.

'I'll buy it,' he said. 'I'll come for it tomorrow evening when I leave the office.'

So the next evening he sat behind the wheel of his big, new car. He drove carefully through the city traffic. When he reached the main road out of the city, he drove faster. The car lights lit the dark road far in front of him. Roger Wingate was very pleased with his new car.

He had to stop at the traffic lights because they were red. He listened happily to the music on the car radio.

Suddenly, his heart jumped. A voice spoke very quietly. It was – or it seemed to be – a woman's voice.

'Turn right here,' it said.

For a minute, Roger thought that the voice came from the radio. He was alone in the car. But the radio was still playing music. And when the voice spoke again, it spoke into his ear. It didn't come from the radio. It seemed to come from the passenger seat next to him.

'Turn right here,' it said again.

It was the voice of a young woman: a clear, light voice. He turned to look at the seat, but the seat was empty, of course. There was nothing to fear. But Roger Wingate was afraid.

Other sounds came from behind him. The drivers of the other cars were angry. Roger looked at the traffic lights. They were green now. He drove away slowly, and the cars went past him. The drivers shouted angrily at him.

But Roger was not thinking about the angry drivers. The sound of that quiet voice was still in his ears: 'Turn right here.' He began to think about the road that went to the right. It seemed to be a quiet street. But it wasn't the way to his house, so he never turned right at the traffic lights.

Roger's wife, Clare, was very pleased with the new car. She thought it was much more comfortable than their old one. 'We'll take my mother out with us at the weekend,' she said. 'We'll take some food and go to the seaside. That will be fun, won't it, Roger?'

He didn't answer. He was looking at the new car through their living-room window.

'Won't it be fun?' she asked again.

'What? Oh ... yes, of course,' he said. 'I'll enjoy that.'

'I can't understand you, Roger,' she said. 'What's the matter? You've just bought this lovely car and you don't seem very pleased.'

'I'm sorry, Clare,' he said. 'I've got a difficult job at the office and I was thinking of that.'

He didn't tell her about the voice in the new car.

◆

Roger left home early the next morning. On his way to the office, he went to see his old friend Bill Harper. Bill worked on a newspaper and he wasn't easily surprised by anything. He listened to Roger's story quietly. Then he asked him a question.

'You don't know that street, then?'

'No,' said Roger.

'If you turn right at those traffic lights, you're in a quiet, narrow little street,' said Bill. 'There are a few trees on each side and some nice houses. It's called Monmouth Road.'

'Have you been there, Bill?'

'Once,' answered Bill. 'About a year ago.'

'You do believe me?' said Roger. 'You believe that I heard that voice?'

'*You* believe that you heard it,' said Bill. 'That's the important thing.'

Bill went to a cupboard and took out a small cassette recorder. He gave it to Roger.

'Carry that in your car on your way home tonight,' he said. 'Switch it on just before you reach the traffic lights. Switch it off when you're past the traffic lights. Bring it back to me tomorrow morning and we'll listen to the cassette together. Promise not to play the cassette before you bring it back.'

'I'll do what you say,' said Roger. 'I need help, Bill. That voice was real to me. It seemed to have a message for me. I don't know what the message was, but ... '

Bill smiled at him. 'It's all right, Roger. I know you're worried about this. I believe your story. I'll help you if I can. We're old friends, remember. Use that cassette recorder on the way home and bring it back tomorrow.'

◆

The next morning Roger put the cassette recorder down on Bill's desk. His face was white.

'Yes,' he said. 'Yes. You needn't ask me. I heard it. Just like last night. But did this thing hear it?' He pointed at the cassette recorder as he spoke. 'If it didn't, you won't believe me.'

'Sit down,' Bill said. 'Let's listen to the cassette. We don't know yet what's on it. When we've heard it, we can try to solve your mystery.'

Roger sat uncomfortably on the front of his chair. 'I didn't use the car radio last night,' he said. 'I didn't want too much noise on the cassette.'

'Good!' said Bill. 'I forgot to tell you not to switch on the radio. I'm glad you thought of that.'

Bill switched the recorder on, and the cassette began to play. At first, they heard only the sounds of the moving car, and the road under the wheels.

'I opened the car window,' Roger explained. 'I needed fresh air.'

'Ssh! Be quiet!' said Bill. 'I guessed that.'

Then there was less noise from the car. It was running very quietly.

'I was slowing down,' said Roger. 'The traffic lights were red. I knew that I had to stop.'

'Quiet, Roger! I understand what's happening.'

Roger closed his eyes and sat back in his chair. He was nervous – no, he was afraid! He was afraid that there was no voice on the cassette. 'Perhaps the recorder didn't work,' he thought. 'Perhaps something went wrong and Bill won't believe me. Then every evening I'll be afraid. I'll be afraid of the time when the voice will speak. And one evening when it speaks, I'll do it. I'll drive my car into the mystery and danger waiting for me in Monmouth Road. Oh, God! The voice must speak now, on the cassette. Bill has to believe me. He has to help me … '

On the cassette the noise of the car disappeared. The car was at the traffic lights. For a second there was almost no sound.

Then came the clear, light voice, and that terrible order: *Turn right here …*

'You heard it!' Roger shouted. 'Bill! You believe me! You must believe me now!'

Bill switched off the cassette recorder. He turned to Roger and spoke very quietly. 'I heard it. I believe you, Roger. She's young. I thought she was.'

'What do you mean?'

'Not now, Roger. I'll explain later. When you've finished at the office, come round here for me. I'm going to travel back with you tonight!'

◆

The car left the city streets behind. Roger drove faster. Bill sat next to him. Neither man spoke. They were nervous ... waiting ...

They saw the traffic lights in front of them. A green light shone towards them.

'What shall I do if the light stays green?' said Roger. 'I've had to stop at it for the past two nights.'

'It won't make any difference,' said Bill. 'She'll speak to you sooner if the light stays green.'

'How do you know?'

'Ssh! Don't talk. Just listen. Then do what she tells you.'

They were nearly at the traffic lights, and the light was still green. Roger's mouth was dry and he could hear the sound of his heart. He looked quickly at his friend. Bill was watching the green light.

Turn right here – it was the same voice, but clearer and stronger.

'Now!' said Bill. 'Into Monmouth Road. And watch! Watch for trouble!'

Roger turned the wheel. The big car turned into the quiet little road. A few street lights formed small lakes of yellow in the darkness. The trees threw deep shadows across the fronts of the houses and on to the road.

A girl was standing in the darkness, under one of the trees. Then the lights of the car fell on her. They could see her clearly. She shone against the blackness of the night. She was young – twenty, twenty-five, perhaps. Beautiful – dressed for a party or a dance.

'This is it!' Bill said. 'Be very careful, Roger!'

The girl threw herself into the road in front of the car. Roger pulled hard at the wheel. The car hit the tree, then stopped.

Roger jumped out of the car. He shouted in a crazy voice, 'My God, I've hit her! I've killed her! Bill! Bill, where are you? Help!'

Bill was by his side. His voice was quiet. 'It's all right, Roger. Don't be afraid. You haven't hurt her. Look! The road is empty. Quiet, now. Be quiet. It's all right.'

'But where ... where's she gone?' said Roger. 'I saw her, she was standing there ... You saw her too ... then she ... '

'Yes, I saw her. And I saw what she did. But she's not here now, Roger. Quiet, now! I'll get a taxi. The garage will come for your car. You can't drive it.'

◆

'I feel better now.' Roger put down his empty coffee cup. 'Please tell us what you know, Bill.'

'Yes, Bill, please explain,' Clare said. 'It's been a terrible night. You and Roger were lucky to escape unhurt.'

'We were.' Bill spoke very slowly. 'Yes, I think she wanted to kill somebody. But I'm not sure that she wanted to kill *us*. I'm not sure of anything.'

'Tell us. Please tell us.'

'I'll try, but it's very difficult. This is a story that I shall never write. Nobody will believe it. I've been in Monmouth Road before. I told you that, Roger, didn't I?'

'Yes,' replied Roger. 'Once, you said. But why did you go there?'

'I didn't want to tell you before,' said Bill. 'Now, I must tell you.' He was silent for a minute, thinking.

'I knew that girl,' he said, at last.

'You did?' said Roger. 'How? Who is she?'

'Wait, please! Listen. Her name is ... ' Bill stopped speaking. Then he started again. 'Her name *was* Kathleen Henson. She was killed in Monmouth Road. But you didn't kill her, Roger. She was killed about a year ago. Her picture was in the newspapers. My paper had a big picture of her. That's how I knew her tonight.'

'I don't remember anything about it.'

'I work for a newspaper, Roger,' said Bill. 'I remember these things. Kathleen Henson lived with her father and mother in a house on Monmouth Road. One night, she was going to a dance with her boyfriend. She was ready, but he wasn't there yet. So she went into the street to wait for him.' Again, he stopped speaking.

'What happened next, Bill?' said Clare.

'Nobody can be quite sure,' he said. 'She stood there and she waited. A car came down Monmouth Road. She thought it was her boyfriend's car, so she ran out into the street. But the car didn't stop. The driver was a stranger. He didn't know that she was waiting for somebody. He didn't slow down. He couldn't. It was too late. He hit her and killed her.'

'What a terrible thing!' cried Clare.

'Yes, it was,' said Bill. 'The police decided that it was an accident. My newspaper sent me to Monmouth Road. I asked a lot of questions, but I couldn't discover any new facts. Now you know why I knew the girl. I've never forgotten her.'

'But Bill, why did Kathleen Henson speak to me?' asked Roger. 'Why did she order me to drive down Monmouth Road?'

'Your car was the car that killed her,' said Bill. 'Listen to me, Roger. Don't ever drive that car again.'

5.1 Were you right?

1 Look back at your answer to Activity 4.4.1. Then tick (✓) the best answers below.

a Where does the voice in the car come from?

☐ The radio.   ☐ The air.

b What does Roger's wife think of the new car?

☐ It is too big.   ☐ It is comfortable.

c What does the cassette player record?

☐ The voice.   ☐ Nothing.

d Who jumps out in front of Roger's car?

☐ Kathleen.   ☐ Kathleen's ghost.

e Why was the car cheap?

☐ Because it killed Kathleen.   ☐ Because of the voice.

2 **Discuss these questions.**

a What do we know about the man who owned the car before Roger?
b Did the garage know the history of the car when they sold it?
c What will Roger do with the car now?

5.2 What more did you learn?

A woman was walking her dog on the other side of Monmouth Road when the accident happened. The police asked her some questions. Write her answers.

POLICE: Did you know Kathleen Henson?	POLICE: What did she do when she saw the car?
WOMAN: Yes, I did. I live in Monmouth Road.	WOMAN: ³ ....
	....
POLICE: What was she doing when you first saw her?	POLICE: Did the car stop?
WOMAN: ¹	WOMAN: ⁴ ....
....	....
POLICE: What happened next?	POLICE: Did the driver slow down?
WOMAN: ² A car	WOMAN: ⁵ ....
....	....
	POLICE: Did you know the driver?
	WOMAN: ⁶ ....
	....

5.3 Language in use

Look at the sentence on the right. Then put the correct word from the box below in each sentence.

> 'We know the man **who** owned it.'

| that | when | where | who |

1 Bill was a man .... wasn't easily surprised by anything.

2 'I'm afraid of the time .... the voice will speak,' said Roger.

3 'This is the place .... the girl was killed,' Bill explained.

4 'This is a story .... I shall never write,' said Bill.

5 'Your car was the car .... killed her,' Bill told Roger.

6 Roger was a man .... didn't believe in ghosts.

5.4 What's next?

Look at the pictures. What do you think is going to happen in the next story? Write your ideas.

A Friend of the Family

'Mrs Frobisher,' she said. 'This is very kind of you.
I've come home again, you know.'

'I know you won't like it. But we can't refuse.' Cecily Frobisher passed a letter to her husband as she spoke. They were sitting at the breakfast table in their big, comfortable kitchen. 'Read it, Frederic,' she said. 'Then you'll see how difficult it is. Susan Blake wants her daughter to stay with us, and I can't refuse.'

'I know how much you like Susan,' said her husband. 'I like her too. But I don't like her husband. He's a terrible man. I don't **trust** him. He tells lies.'

'I don't trust him, either,' said Cecily. 'But Terence Blake isn't coming here to stay. Please read the letter, Frederic, then you'll understand. Their daughter, Isobel, must come.'

Frederic Frobisher read Susan Blake's letter carefully. Susan's husband, Terence, had a well-paid job in Canada, and they needed the money. He was in Canada already, and she wanted to join him there. But Isobel was only sixteen, and she was still at school. Her mother wanted her to stay at school in England until she was eighteen. Could Isobel live with the Frobishers until then? The Frobishers were the only real friends that Susan had. Isobel's grandparents were all dead.

Frederic Frobisher passed the letter back to his wife. 'I feel sorry for Susan,' he said.

'I do too, Frederic,' said Cecily. 'She must join Terence soon. This is the first good job that he's had for years.'

'And if she doesn't join him, he'll do something silly,' said Frederic. 'He'll lose the job. You can't trust him. His wife doesn't trust him!' Frederic was angry. 'He wasn't honest with us when he sold us this house.'

'That was ten years ago,' Cecily said. 'And we've been very happy here.'

He smiled at her. 'We've always been happy together, my dear. And this is a lovely house. But Terence Blake told lies about it, and the price was too high.'

'Perhaps he didn't want to sell it,' she said. 'His parents lived here. Blakes have lived here for hundreds of years.'

'He *had* to sell it. He was stupid and spent all his money. So he had to sell the house.'

Cecily put her hand on her husband's arm. 'Let's stop talking about Terence now, dear. I agree with you about him. But what shall I tell Susan?'

---

trust /trʌst/ (v) to believe that someone is honest. They will not lie to you or hurt you.

Frederic Frobisher was quiet for a minute. Then he said slowly, 'I've told you already, I feel sorry for Susan. I'd like to help her.'

'Then shall I tell her that Isobel can come?'

Her husband looked at his watch. 'It's late,' he said. 'I should be at work.' He turned to his wife. 'You'd like the girl to come here, wouldn't you?' he asked.

'Yes, Frederic,' she said. 'I haven't seen Isobel for a long time, but she was a nice little girl. It will be fun to have her with us. And she *is* a friend of the family.'

Frederic smiled. 'Write today, Cecily. Invite her to come. We'll try to make her happy.'

He left the kitchen and closed the door after him. She heard him walk across to his library. He was writing a new book. He worked in the library every morning.

'Isobel won't be in the way,' she said to herself. 'The house is big. There's plenty of room for all of us.'

♦

About a month later, on a dark December evening, Cecily Frobisher waited in the **hall** alone. Her husband was on his way to the railway station to meet Isobel Blake's train. She looked round the hall. A warm fire was burning and all the lights were on. She wanted the house to welcome Isobel.

Then she suddenly felt ill. She could hear the sound of her heart in her chest, and her head was hurting her. She sat down in a chair near the fire.

'Cecily Frobisher, you *are* a silly woman!' she said to herself. 'You're nervous because a sixteen-year-old girl is coming to stay with you. How silly! What are you afraid of? You have a loving husband who writes very popular books. You have a beautiful home. You're well and happy. Now, rest until Isobel arrives.'

She fell asleep in her comfortable chair by the warm fire, and she dreamed. In her dream she could see herself, asleep in the chair. And she saw the library door open. An old woman came through the door. She was wearing a long black dress and her hair was white. She walked slowly across the hall to the fire, and turned her face to the sleeping woman. Her mouth opened.

'Don't!' Cecily cried out. 'Don't speak! Don't speak to me! I won't listen to you!'

hall /hɔːl/ (n) the area inside the front door of a building. You walk through the *hall* to reach other rooms.

Her own shout woke her. She jumped to her feet. The hall was empty. Then the front door opened, and she heard a girl's voice. 'I know the way in. I can walk around this house in the dark.'

Frederic and Isobel came towards her. He was carrying the girl's suitcase and smiling.

'The train was late, Cecily. It's a cold, wet night. Take Isobel up to her room. I'll bring her suitcase up, then we'll have dinner. I'm sure Isobel is hungry.'

Isobel was tall, dark and quite thin. Her eyes were bright and excited. She spoke quickly, but she wasn't nervous.

'Mrs Frobisher,' she said. 'This is very kind of you. I've come home again, you know.'

Her words were polite. Cecily tried to answer them, but she felt uncomfortable. She felt strange in her own house. Was this girl the visitor – or was she?

Isobel looked round the hall. 'It's different,' she said. 'You've made changes.'

'Well, we've–' began Cecily.

'Of course, it's full of light and it's warm,' said Isobel. 'We never had a fire in the hall. It was too expensive. But you're rich.'

'No,' said Cecily. She tried to speak quietly. 'No, Isobel, we *aren't* rich. We have enough ... '

'Which room are you giving me?' Again, Isobel didn't wait to hear Cecily's words.

'You'll sleep in the big front bedroom. It has a lovely view of the garden. I thought you'd like ... '

'Yes, thank you,' said Isobel. 'That always was my room. Don't come up with me. I know the way.'

And she ran up the stairs. Frederic followed slowly, with her suitcase in his hand. Cecily stood and watched them.

When Frederic returned to the hall, his wife was looking into the fire. He came towards her and she turned round.

'I've made a great mistake, Frederic,' she said.

'Oh, it's too soon to say that,' he said. 'Everything's strange. We like a quiet life. It'll be all right.'

He was trying to calm her, but he was nervous too.

◆

After a week, Cecily became more hopeful. Perhaps Isobel's visit wasn't a mistake. The girl helped with the cooking. She joined in the conversation at meals. She went to bed early, and she was often upstairs in her room. She seemed happy in her new life.

'I'm afraid you must be lonely,' Cecily said to her one day. They were in the kitchen. Lunch was nearly ready. 'You'll make friends when you go to your new school. It's a lonely life for a young girl in this big house.'

'Lonely!' Isobel smiled at her. 'I'm not lonely, Mrs Frobisher. I can't be lonely here.'

'That's kind of you, my dear.' Cecily was pleased. 'But you do need friends of your own age.'

'I don't need any young friends. I already have all the friends that I need here.'

'Thank you, dear,' said Cecily. 'But Frederic and I are much too old to be ...'

'Oh, I wasn't thinking of you and your husband.'

'What do you mean, Isobel? Who ... ?'

The girl left the room before Cecily could finish her question. Cecily heard her laugh softly as she walked across the hall.

After supper that night, Frederic and Cecily Frobisher sat by the fire. Isobel was upstairs in her room. Cecily spoke first, very quietly. She was afraid to speak loudly.

'You don't look well, Frederic,' she said. 'What's the matter?

'It's difficult to explain, Cecily,' he said. 'It's silly of me, I know. But I haven't been able to write since Isobel came here.'

'But she doesn't make a noise. I sometimes think that she's too quiet.'

'Oh no, it's not Isobel ... ' He stopped. He looked afraid.

'Tell me, Frederic. Please tell me.'

'I must be quiet and alone when I'm writing a book,' he said. 'You know that. So my library is very important to me. It's big and quiet and comfortable. My books are there. I can sit at my desk and write for hours.'

'I know, dear. But nothing has changed. You go into the library every morning after breakfast and you stay there until lunch.'

'Yes,' he said. 'And I haven't written anything. Oh, I've tried. But I can't think about my work. I'm not alone in there.'

'Not alone! What do you mean, Frederic? I never come into the library when you're busy. I'm sure Isobel doesn't. Does she?'

'No, she hasn't been in. But when I sit in my writing chair, I can hear a voice. I think it's a woman's voice – an old woman's voice. She's talking, but I can't hear the words. The room doesn't seem to belong to me now. My desk isn't mine. My chair isn't mine. Nothing in my library is mine.'

'Frederic! Stop!' cried Cecily. 'You're frightening me. You need a rest – a holiday. We must ... '

She stopped speaking as a shadow fell across her face. She looked up. Isobel was standing on the stairs.

'What do you want? Why are you moving so quietly?' Fear made Cecily's voice angry.

'I always move quietly,' the girl answered. Was she smiling at them? 'You like the house to be quiet. I was thirsty. I came down to get a glass of water.'

'Then get it and go back to your room.'

'Yes, Mrs Frobisher.'

A minute later, Isobel returned from the kitchen. She put the glass down and stood between them. 'You never saw my grandmother, did you?' she said.

'*I* didn't,' Frederic answered. 'And I don't think my wife did. We didn't visit this house when you lived here. Your mother came to stay with us once or twice, but we didn't come here.'

'My grandmother lived here with us when I was a little girl. I loved her very much. She told me a lot of stories about the house. It's very old, you know. She died here. Then my father lost his money and you bought our house.'

'It was very sad for you, Isobel,' said Frederic, 'but ... '

'Oh, don't be sorry for me. I'm back now. My grandmother promised me. "This house will be yours," she said.' Isobel smiled again. Nobody spoke for a minute or two. Then she said, 'Can I use your library, Mr Frobisher? It was my grandmother's special room. She didn't like other people to use it. Except me. She liked me to sit in there with her. I sat there and listened to her stories. I'll be very quiet. I was always quiet in there.'

'But ... I don't think ... no ... ' Frederic stopped. He looked across at his wife. Her hands were covering her face.

'Don't try to decide now,' said Isobel. 'You can give me your answer in the morning. I must go to bed now. Oh, I nearly forgot. Here's a photograph of my grandmother. I brought it downstairs with me. I'm sure it will interest you, Mrs Frobisher.' Isobel pushed the photograph into Cecily's hands. 'Look at it. Perhaps you know the face.'

Cecily looked at the photograph. Her face went white and her cry of fear rang through the quiet room. It was a picture of the old woman from her dream.

◆

The Frobishers didn't sleep that night. They lay in bed and talked in quiet voices.

'What can we do, Frederic?' said Cecily. 'She must go away. She's pushing us out of our house.'

'She's not going to get me out.'

'But she's not alone. That terrible old woman is here helping her. Remember what Isobel said. Her grandmother promised her the house. She'll take it away from us.'

'That's impossible,' said Frederic. 'It's our house. We bought it. And how can the old woman be here? She's dead.'

'Then why aren't you alone in the library? Who's in there with you? Why did I know the woman in that photograph?'

'But, Cecily ... '

'Ssh! Listen!'

They heard the library door open. Then it closed. Slow footsteps crossed the hall. Somebody – or something – climbed the stairs. They heard the footsteps go past their bedroom door. Then Isobel's bedroom door opened and closed. And in the darkness, they could hear voices.

Cecily took her husband's hand. 'Take me away tomorrow, Frederic. I'm frightened.'

'We'll go tomorrow morning, my dear. But Isobel must come with us. We can't leave her here alone.'

When it was light, Frederic dressed. 'Put some things in a suitcase,' he said. 'We can stay at the hotel in the village for a day or two. I'll wake Isobel.'

Before Cecily was ready, he was back. 'Hurry!' he said. 'Leave that suitcase. Isobel isn't in her room.'

'Not in her room! Where is she?'

Frederic hurried his wife downstairs and out of the house before he answered. 'The library door's locked. I can't get in. But Isobel's in there. And she's talking to someone.'

He drove to the village and left Cecily at the hotel.

'You'll be safe here,' he said. 'Wait until I come back.'

'Where are you going, Frederic?'

'I'm going to get a police officer and the doctor,' he said. 'Then I'm going back to our house – if it is our house.'

◆

The police officer looked closely at the lock on the library door.

'I shall have to break a window and climb into the room,' he said. 'That lock is too strong to break.'

Frederic Frobisher and the doctor waited in the hall in front of the library door. They heard the sound of breaking glass. They heard the key turn, and the door opened.

'Come in, doctor,' said the police officer. 'No, not you, Mr Frobisher. It's not nice in there.'

Frederic could hear the sound of his heart while he waited. And he could hear noises in the library. The police officer spoke. A chair was moved. The doctor said something. The minutes seemed like hours.

Then the library door opened again, and the doctor came out. He put a hand on Frederic's arm and took him to a chair at the other end of the hall.

'She's dead, Mr Frobisher,' he said. 'She's sitting in the big writing chair. *How* old is she?'

'Sixteen, doctor. She had her sixteenth birthday just before she came to live with us.'

'Sixteen! Then what's happened to her? Her hair is white, and her face is the face of an old woman.'

49

6.1 Were you right?

1 **Look back at Activity 5.4. Then put a cross (✗) next to the two sentences that are not true.**

a ☐ The Blakes owned the house that the Frobishers live in.

b ☐ The Frobishers invite Isobel to live with them.

c ☐ Isobel feels at home as soon as she arrives in the house.

d ☐ Frederic hears an old woman's voice when he is alone in the library.

e ☐ Only Isobel and her grandmother used the library when they lived in the house.

f ☐ Cecily sees the old woman walking past her bedroom door.

g ☐ Isobel locks herself in the library.

h ☐ Frederic takes Cecily to the hotel in the village.

i ☐ A police officer breaks into the library from the garden.

j ☐ Isobel is dead in the library.

2 **Discuss these questions.**

a What happened to Isobel in the library?

b Will the Frobishers go back and live in the house? Why (not)?

c What will the Frobishers tell Susan and Terence Blake?

6.2 What more did you learn?

What do we know about these people? Match the information to the names.

1 Terence Blake

doesn't trust her husband.

2 Isobel Blake

has a well-paid job in Canada.

3 Frederic Frobisher

has two more years at school.

4 Susan Blake

likes a quiet life.

5 Old Mrs Blake

used the library as her special room.

6 Cecily Frobisher

writes popular books.

5.3 Language in use

Look at the sentence on the right. Then use the verbs to complete these first conditional sentences.

> If she **doesn't join** him, he**'ll do** something silly.

1 If we .... (not say) yes, Susan .... (not be able) to go to Canada.

2 If Isobel .... (come) to live with us, it .... (be) fun.

3 If you .... (get) the dinner ready, I .... (take) Isobel's suitcase upstairs.

4 If Isobel .... (make) friends at school, she .... (not be) lonely.

5 If she .... (stay), she .... (push) us out of our house.

5.4 What's next?

Look at the title of the next story and the words in *italics* below it. Look at the picture on page 53. Which of these letters is the woman waiting for?

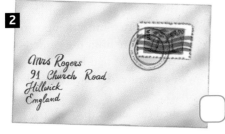

A Birthday Card for Mrs Rogers

I walked slowly up the garden path of Number 91. I searched through my bag, but I couldn't find any letters for that address.

I picked up my bag of letters, left the post office and started my long ride through the streets of Hillwick. It was seven o'clock on a sunny summer morning. The bright morning made me happy, but there was another reason for my happiness. My wife and I were from London. But when Hillwick was looking for a postman, I decided to take the job. Now, six weeks later, we had a comfortable little house with a good garden. We liked the quiet, sleepy little town, and we already had some friends.

I've always liked my work. I like fresh air and exercise. And people need postmen to carry their letters safely. The business life of the country stops if letters aren't delivered. But I really like delivering the private letters. People write to their old friends. Adult children write to their parents. Boys write to the girls they love. It makes me happy to carry these letters.

I was thinking of all those things as I rode my bicycle down Gold Street on that bright summer morning. Most of the buildings were shops and offices, and I delivered letters to them all. My bag was much lighter when I turned left into Church Road.

Not many of the houses in Church Road had letters that morning, so I soon arrived at the last house, Number 92. I had three letters for that address. When I opened the gate to the front garden, I heard a voice.

'You've forgotten my letter, postman.'

The voice came from the garden of Number 91. A woman was standing in front of the door of that house.

'Wait a minute,' I answered. 'I'll deliver these letters to Number 92, then I'll come back.'

I pushed the letters through the letterbox of Number 92, and then I walked slowly up the garden path of Number 91. I searched through my bag, but I couldn't find any letters for that address.

The woman stood waiting for me with a little smile on her face. She seemed sure that I had a letter for her. She put out her hand and I could see a big gold ring on her finger. Her grey hair was bright in the sunlight. She was wearing a dark green dress, and shiny shoes. I searched through my bag again.

'Perhaps it's a card,' she said. 'Sometimes he sends me a letter and sometimes he sends me a card.'

Her voice was soft, and her big brown eyes watched me.

'A card or a letter,' she said. 'From my son in America. He lives there now, but he never forgets my birthday. It's my birthday today, postman.'

'I hope you'll have a happy ... ' I wanted her to be happy. I wanted her to have her letter. But I knew that I didn't have one for her.

'Please look again, postman,' she said. 'A letter or card for Mrs Emily Rogers of 91, Church Road.'

I looked through my bag again. I knew there was no mistake. There was nothing for Mrs Rogers, but I didn't want to make her sad.

I felt angry with her son. It was wrong of him to forget his mother's birthday. I couldn't tell her that. But that's what I thought.

At last, I had to speak. 'I'm sorry, Mrs Rogers. There's nothing here for you. Perhaps ... tomorrow ... I'm sorry ... '

The happy smile was gone, and I saw tears in her eyes. Suddenly, she looked very small and very old.

'Something's happened to him,' she said. Her voice was very weak. 'He's never forgotten before.'

She turned away from me. When I reached the gate, I looked back. The front door of Number 91 was closing.

I delivered the rest of the letters and cards in my bag and I returned to the post office. My morning's work was finished and I was free until six o'clock that evening. Then I had to go to the railway station with the letters that were posted in Hillwick.

I started to ride my bicycle down Sheep Street, but I stopped at a little café for a cup of coffee. What a sad birthday for Mrs Rogers! I wanted to make her happy again. But how?

Then I had an idea. I went to a newspaper shop where they sold birthday cards. I chose a card for Mrs Rogers.

I chose the birthday card very carefully. It was a copy of a picture by Turner, the great English painter. Inside, there was a simple message: 'Happy Birthday'. Below the message, I wrote, 'For Mrs Rogers. I hope that I shall bring you a card from your son tomorrow.' Then I signed my name and added, 'Your Postman'.

I felt better after that. It wasn't a birthday card from her son, of course. But it was a card, on her birthday. Somebody was thinking about her.

At the bottom of Gold Street, I turned left into Church Road. A big lorry was parked outside one of the houses. The traffic wasn't moving, and I had to wait.

I thought about the day's problems while I waited. Why wasn't I at home now, working in my garden? Why was I trying to look after Mrs Rogers?

'And why haven't I seen her before?' I asked myself. 'I've worked in Hillwick and delivered letters in Church Road for six weeks now. But there haven't been any letters for Number 91. I haven't seen Mrs Rogers at her door, or in her garden. It's strange.'

But I had no answers. The traffic began to move, and I rode to Mrs Rogers' house.

I got off my bicycle at her garden gate. While I walked up the garden path, I tried to solve another problem. 'Shall I push the card through the letterbox and walk away?' I asked myself. 'No, that's not very friendly. It's her birthday. She'll want to talk to somebody.'

So I knocked loudly on her door. I held the card out in front of me and I waited for the door to open.

'You won't get an answer there, postman.'

The voice came from the next garden. A woman was looking at me. She lived in Number 92, and her name was Sparson. I knew this from her letters.

'I don't understand ... ' I said.

'That house is empty,' she said.

'I've got a birthday card for Mrs Rogers,' I said. 'It's her birthday today.'

'I know it is,' she said. 'Or ... I know it was.'

'Was?' I asked. 'What do you mean?'

'Number 91 is empty. Nobody's lived there for a year.'

'But I saw Mrs Rogers this morning. She was waiting for me. She told me about her birthday. She was hoping for a card from her son. He lives in America.'

'He *did* live in America.' Mrs Sparson's voice seemed louder. 'A year ago today, Mrs Rogers was waiting for a birthday card from her son. He never forgot her birthday. The card didn't arrive, but later that day she had a phone call from New York. Her son was dead. Killed in a car accident.'

'What terrible news!' I said. 'And on her birthday!'

'It was,' said Mrs Sparson. 'She died that evening, of a broken heart.'

I stood there for a minute. Then I put Mrs Rogers' birthday card in my pocket and I walked slowly to the garden gate.

Talk about it

1 Discuss which is the most frightening story in this book. Which is the least frightening? Why?

2 What are you afraid of? Look at this list and add two more ideas. Then put the list in order from the most frightening (1) to the least frightening (8).

- [ ] a loud scream behind a closed door
- [ ] a light suddenly going on and off
- [ ] a phone ringing, but there is no one at the other end
- [ ] a frightening laugh in the night
- [ ] a voice talking very quietly in the corner of a room
- [ ] a strange light moving across the wall
- [ ] ....
- [ ] ....

3 Look at this photograph of a 'ghost'. The photograph was taken in 1863.

a How was the picture made, do you think?

b Does it look real? Is it frightening?

c When you imagine a ghost, is it like this? How is it different from this one?

d Imagine what happened before this. What is going to happen next? Tell the story.

Describe what is happening in the pictures. Then use your ideas to finish the story.

1 ....

2 ....

3 ....

4 ....

NOW FINISH THE STORY.

....

....

1 Work with two other students. You have gone out for the day together. Where are you? Choose one of these places.

A

You are waiting for the last train at a station. There is nobody on the platform. It is late, dark and cold.

B

You are looking around an old house in the country. There was a fire at the house, and parts of it are falling down. Nobody lives there now.

C

You are walking in wild, open country. You are following one lonely road, but there are no cars. You can hear horses on the road, but you can't see them. It is getting late.

D

You are running through a city park for your evening exercise. The street lights are lit. It is winter and it has snowed. Why aren't you at home by the fire?

E

You are going back to your car after eating out in the city. Your car is on the top floor of a four-floor car park. There are lots of dark stairs.

F

Your idea.

2 **Suddenly you all see a ghost. What is it like? Talk about these ghosts, and choose one.**

A

It moves things about and sometimes it throws them.

B

It carries its head under its arm.

C

You can hear it but you never see it.

D

You can see through it. It can move through stone walls. It can fly up and down stairs.

E

A priest caught it in a bottle. It can't get out.

F

Your ideas.

3 **You find out the history of your ghost. Decide on answers to these questions.**

Who was your ghost when it was alive?

....

What did it do?

....

Why can't it rest?

....

Where does it spend its time?

....

What does it do when it sees someone?

....

What do people do when they see it?

....

4 **Your ghost wants to leave this world. How do you help it?**

....

....

5 **Get ready to talk about your ghost. Say where you saw it. Talk about what it is like. Describe its history. How can it leave this world? Which of you is going to say what? Make notes here.**

Notes

Student A

Student B

Student C

6 **Take turns to tell the class about your ghosts. The class should decide on:**

- the most frightening ghost
- the silliest ghost
- the most believable story
- the least believable story